Now you
flute solo
recorded arrangements

Classical
COLLECTION

TAKE
THE
LEAD

flute

IMP

International MUSIC Publications

International Music Publications Limited
Griffin House 161 Hammersmith Road London W6 8BS England

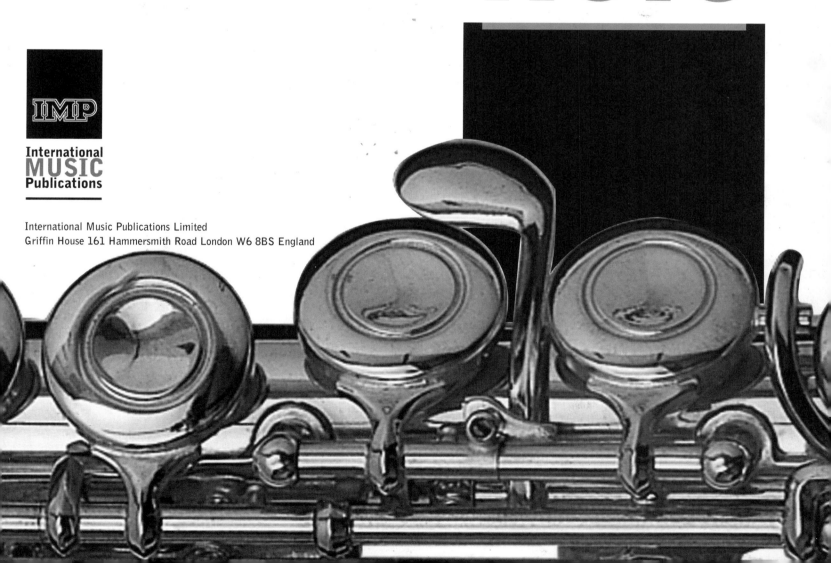

Series Editor: Anna Joyce

Editorial, production and recording: Artemis Music Limited
Design and production: Space DPS Limited

Published 2000

International **MUSIC** Publications

© International Music Publications Limited
Griffin House 161 Hammersmith Road London W6 8BS England

Exclusive Distributors:

International Music Publications Limited

England:	Griffin House 161 Hammersmith Road London W6 8BS
Germany:	Marstallstr. 8 D-80539 München
Denmark:	Danmusik Vognmagergade 7 DK1120 Copenhagen K

Italy:	Nuova Carisch Srl Via Campania 12 20098 San Giuliano Milanese Milano
Spain:	Nueva Carisch España Magallanes 25 28015 Madrid
France:	Carisch Musicom 25 Rue d'Hauteville 75010 Paris

WARNER BROS. PUBLICATIONS U.S. INC.

USA:	15800 N.W. 48th Avenue Miami, Florida 33014

Australia:	3 Talavera Road North Ryde New South Wales 2113
Scandinavia:	P.O. Box 533 Vendevägen 85 B S-182 15 Danderyd Sweden

flute

TAKE THE LEAD

In the Book...

On the CD...

Demonstration

Backing

Dance Of
The Sugar Plum Fairy

(from *The Nutcracker*)

Music by Peter Ilyich Tchaikovsky

8

Demonstration

Backing

Radetzky March

Music by Johann Strauss Snr

Moderate march tempo

mf *sempre staccato*

Demonstration

Backing

In The Hall
Of The Mountain King

(from *Peer Gynt*)

Music by Edvard Grieg

accel. al fine

Demonstration

Backing

Polovtsian Dance

(from *Prince Igor*)

Music by Alexander Borodin

Gently

Demonstration

Backing

Sheep May Safely Graze

Music by Johann Sebastian Bach

Demonstration

Backing

Symphony No.40
in G minor, 1st movement

Music by Wolfgang Amadeus Mozart

The Swan

(from *Carnival of the Animals*)

Music by Camille Saint-Säens

Demonstration

Backing

The Toreador's Song

(from *Carmen*)

Music by Georges Bizet

You can be the featured soloist with
TAKE THE LEAD

Collect these titles, each with demonstration and full backing tracks on CD.

90s Hits

The Air That I Breathe	(Simply Red)
Angels	(Robbie Williams)
How Do I Live	(LeAnn Rimes)
I Don't Want To Miss A Thing	(Aerosmith)
I'll Be There For You	(The Rembrandts)
My Heart Will Go On	(Celine Dion)
Something About The Way	
You Look Tonight	(Elton John)
Frozen	(Madonna)

Order ref: 6725A – Flute
Order ref: 6726A – Clarinet
Order ref: 6727A – Alto Saxophone
Order ref: 6728A – Violin

Movie Hits

Because You Loved Me	(Up Close And Personal)
Blue Monday	(The Wedding Singer)
(Everything I Do)	
I Do It For You	(Robin Hood: Prince Of Thieves)
I Don't Want To Miss A Thing	(Armageddon)
I Will Always Love You	(The Bodyguard)
Star Wars (Main Title)	(Star Wars)
The Wind Beneath My Wings	(Beaches)
You Can Leave Your Hat On	(The Full Monty)

Order ref: 6908A – Flute
Order ref: 6909A – Clarinet
Order ref: 6910A – Alto Saxophone
Order ref: 6911A –Tenor Saxophone
Order ref: 6912A – Violin

TV Themes

- Coronation Street
- I'll Be There For You (theme from *Friends*)
- Match Of The Day
- (Meet) The Flintstones
- Men Behaving Badly
- Peak Practice
- The Simpsons
- The X-Files

Order ref: 7003A – Flute
Order ref: 7004A – Clarinet
Order ref: 7005A – Alto Saxophone
Order ref: 7006A – Violin

Christmas Songs

- The Christmas Song
- (Chestnuts Roasting On An Open Fire)
- Frosty The Snowman
- Have Yourself A Merry Little Christmas
- Little Donkey
- Rudolph The Red-Nosed Reindeer
- Santa Claus Is Comin' To Town
- Sleigh Ride
- Winter Wonderland

Order ref: 7022A – Flute
Order ref: 7023A – Clarinet
Order ref: 7024A – Alto Saxophone
Order ref: 7025A – Violin
Order ref: 7026A – Piano
Order ref: 7027A – Drums

The Blues Brothers

- She Caught The Katy And Left Me A Mule To Ride
- Gimme Some Lovin'
- Shake A Tail Feather
- Everybody Needs Somebody To Love
- The Old Landmark
- Think
- Minnie The Moocher
- Sweet Home Chicago

Order ref: 7079A - Flute
Order ref: 7080A - Clarinet
Order ref: 7081A - Alto Saxophone
Order ref: 7082A - Tenor Saxophone
Order ref: 7083A - Trumpet
Order ref: 7084A - Violin

Latin

- Bailamos
- Cherry Pink And Apple Blossom White
- Guantanamera
- La Bamba
- La Isla Bonita
- Livin' La Vida Loca
- Oye Mi Canto (Hear My Voice)
- Soul Limbo

Order ref: 7259A - Flute
Order ref: 7260A - Clarinet
Order ref: 7261A - Alto Saxophone
Order ref: 7364A - Piano
Order ref: 7262A - Trumpet
Order ref: 7263A - Violin

Jazz

- Birdland
- Desafinado
- Don't Get Around Much Anymore
- Fascinating Rhythm
- Misty
- My Funny Valentine
- One O'Clock Jump
- Summertime

Order ref: 7124A - Flute
Order ref: 7173A - Clarinet
Order ref: 7174A - Alto Saxophone
Order ref: 7175A - Tenor Saxophone
Order ref: 7179A - Drums
Order ref: 7178A - Piano
Order ref: 7176A - Trumpet
Order ref: 7177A - Violin

Swing

- Chattanooga Choo Choo
- Choo Choo Ch'Boogie
- I've Got A Gal In Kalamazoo
- In The Mood
- It Don't Mean A Thing (If It Ain't Got That Swing)
- Jersey Bounce
- Pennsylvania 6-5000
- A String Of Pearls

Order ref: 7235A - Flute
Order ref: 7236A - Clarinet
Order ref: 7237A - Alto Saxophone
Order ref: 7238A - Tenor Saxophone
Order ref: 7239A - Trumpet
Order ref: 7240A - Violin